Based on the characters by
Julia Donaldson and Axel Scheffler

THE GRUFFALO and Friends

Outdoor Activity Book

Activities created by
Little Wild Things

MACMILLAN CHILDREN'S BOOKS

Contents

The Gruffalo

Monkey Puzzle

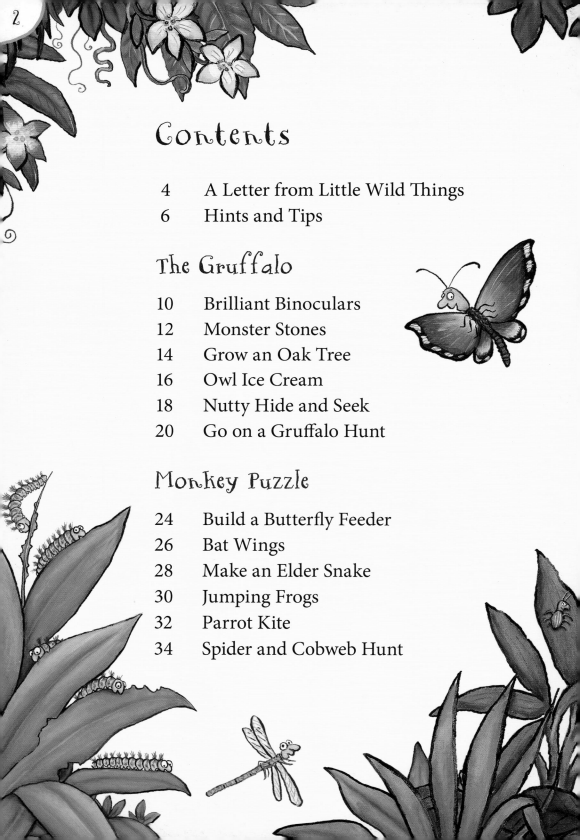

Room on the Broom

Charlie Cook's Favourite Book

A Letter from Little Wild Things

Dear adventurers,

We are Little Wild Things, a small community organisation running outdoor nature play sessions for children in a West Oxfordshire woodland. We spend our days outside with local families sploshing in mud, mixing up potions, digging for treasure and racing snails and we really can't think of anything we'd enjoy more.

Children today spend less time playing outdoors than ever before, so we want to spread the word that outdoor play is fun and easy. Most of us have a bit of grass or patch of muddy ground within walking distance, and there is always something exciting going on in the natural world. Birds might be singing, leaves might be falling, or there might just be hundreds of huge puddles to jump in. Playing outside together is fun and free and is likely to lead to healthier, happier children. But the best thing? Nature is something you can never grow out of.

This book is a collection of some of our favourite outdoor adventures based on four much-loved picture books by Julia Donaldson and Axel Scheffler. Use them for a party, in the

school holidays, on a walk, or on a rainy day. Get outside and go wild, and we hope you have as much fun with them as we do.

little wild things

Hints and Tips

Are you ready to get adventuring? Here are some hints and tips to read before you start.

You'll need to ask a grown-up to help you set up and lend a hand here and there.

Before you start any activity, read through the instructions with your grown-up and gather all the things you need for your adventure kit. You'll find a list at the beginning of every activity.

Ask your grown-up to help with anything you find especially difficult. Cutting things out with scissors, folding or measuring can all be hard work. Sometimes you'll just need your grown-up to show you what to do and, with a bit of practice, you'll be doing it by yourself in no time.

Your outdoors doesn't have to be big and wild! Any garden, park or patch of outside space will do for lots of the activities in this book.

Sometimes you'll want to collect things from your garden or park or dig in a flower bed. Check with a grown-up that you are allowed to do those things before you start.

Remember it's always best to collect things that are on the ground rather than picking living flowers and plants. For example, you should always take sticks from the ground rather than pulling them off trees.

It's great to get messy, and lots of these activities involve mud, so it's best not to try them when you're wearing your smartest clothes! Also, be sure to give your hands a good wash with hot water and soap when you've finished playing.

Lots of the things you can make in this book might look delicious, but remember anything you make outdoors is not for eating.

Take care of your friends if you're running, jumping or swishing things around. Make sure you have plenty of space so you don't bang, bash or bump them by mistake.

Now you know all there is to know and you're ready to start adventuring! What will you do first?

THE GRUFFALO

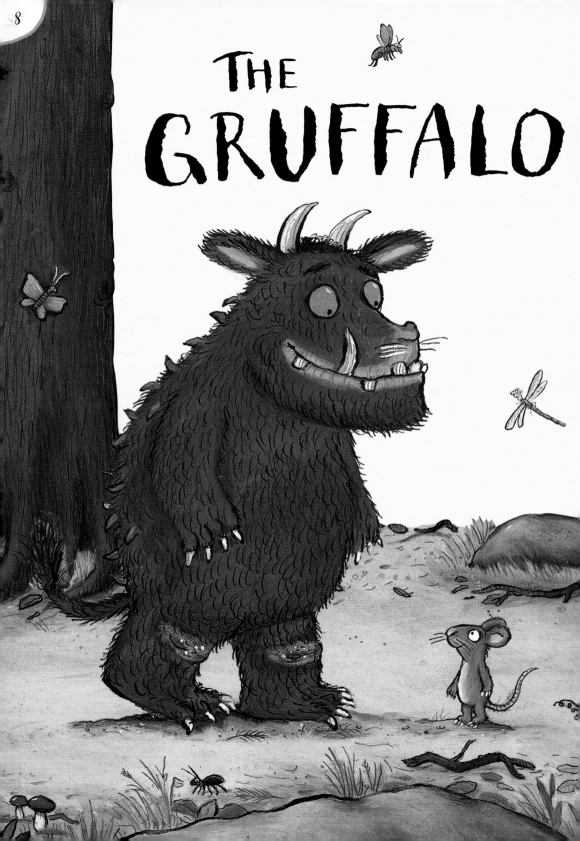

A mouse took a stroll through the deep dark wood.
A fox saw the mouse and the mouse looked good.

When a little mouse comes face to face with a fox,
an owl and a snake who all want to eat him up, he
makes up a monster to scare them away, but then
has to think fast when he discovers that his
monster – the Gruffalo – really does exist . . .

Read on to find out how to make a pair of
woodland binoculars, play some monster games
and get ideas for your very own Gruffalo hunt!

Brilliant Binoculars

Binoculars are super for spotting the Gruffalo, mice and all sorts of other animals, so why not make some to take on your next adventure?

Adventure kit:

- A piece of A4 card
- Colouring pencils
- Sticky tape
- Safety scissors
- String (as long as your arm)

What to do:

1. Take the card and fold it in half, bringing the short sides together, then do this again. Now open up your card and cut along the fold lines to make four equal rectangles.

2. Decorate two rectangles with your colouring pencils (save the other two for your grown-up or a friend). You could draw patterns, animals, or even make your binoculars camouflaged!

3. Take one piece of card and roll it into a tube by bringing the short sides together, with the decorations on the outside.

4. Stick the edges of the tube together with sticky tape.

5. Do the same with your other decorated piece of card so that you have two tubes.

6. Stand the tubes up so they are touching and use more sticky tape to wrap around both tubes so they are stuck together. Ask a grown-up to help if you need another pair of hands.

7. Take one end of the string and poke it through one of the tubes. Then poke it back through the other tube and tie the ends together. This is your neck strap.

8. Pop the strap over your head and hold your binoculars to your eyes. What can you see?

Hints and tips:

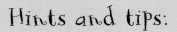

To get the most out of your binoculars you want to be looking down the centre of both tubes. For little eyes this might mean rolling the tubes tighter so they sit closer together – making them easier to see through.

Your binoculars are wonderful for spotting the Gruffalo but they can make it tricky to see your feet! Do watch out if you are walking and looking at the same time.

Keep adventuring:

Try taking your binoculars out on a walk to see what you can spot. Find a good place to keep watch and stay quiet and still and you never know what you might see – even if you don't spot the Gruffalo, the world is full of birds, squirrels and insects just waiting to be seen!

Monster Stones

Mouse makes up a monster to scare away Snake, Owl and Fox. Make up your own monster with this game – and let's hope it doesn't turn out to be real!

Adventure Kit:
At least twenty plain smooth stones, no smaller than a coin and no bigger than your hand, and some paints or felt tip pens.

What to do:

1. Paint or draw a terrible monster feature on each stone.
   You will need a mixture of:

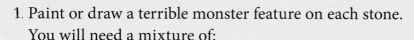

nasty noses   enormous ears   scary hair

evil eyes   monster mouths with terrible teeth

And don't forget to make all your features truly monstrous . . .
You might like to include:

terrible tongues   wicked warts   hideous horns

beastly brows   poisonous pimples

2. Once you've done as many stones as you want, leave them to dry. Then mix them up and turn them all over so you can't see the features.

3. Choose ten stones at random.

4. Make a monster face using the stones you have chosen. How scary can you make it? Will your face have one eye, two tongues or only noses?!

5. Play the game with a friend and see who can make the most fearsome monster.

Hints and tips:

- Marker pens work well on stones but remember they will also mark your skin so check with a grown-up before using them.

- Twenty stones is good for two players, but you may need to design some more if you have more than one friend who wants to play.

Keep adventuring:

If you enjoyed making monster faces, why not find some more stones and try drawing some other monster body parts? Tummies, tails, tusks, spikes, paws or claws – just let your imagination run wild!

Grow an Oak Tree

Trees are not just for the deep dark wood –
why not try growing one at home?

Adventure kit:

- A bucket of water
- A clear plastic bag
- Damp soil or compost
- A plate
- A lolly stick
- A pen
- A little pot with a hole in the bottom

What to do:

1. First find an oak tree and then look for some acorns on the ground. Choose acorns that are fat, brown and ripe (rather than green) and have no cracks or beetle holes in them.

2. Test your acorns by dropping them in a bucket of water. Nuts that are good for planting should sink. If any float, pick them out and throw them away.

3. Fish out the acorns that have sunk to the bottom and drop them in a clear bag with a few handfuls of damp soil or compost. Seal the bag and put it in the back of the fridge.

4. Check your acorns after two weeks to see if they have started growing roots. If not, leave them in the fridge for another week or so until they do.

5. Once you have some acorns with roots, it's time for planting! Fill a little pot halfway with soil. Make a hole in the soil and pop an acorn in with the root facing down, then cover it with more soil.

6. On the top half of your lolly stick, draw four horizontal lines about 1cm apart. Push the blank half of the lolly stick into the soil so the half with the lines you've drawn is sticking out.

7. Put the pot on a plate and give your acorn a drink of water. The soil should feel damp but not too soggy. Give your acorn a little drink every few days, and keep an eye on it to see when the first shoots start to show.

8. Once a shoot has pushed its way out of the soil, you can see how quickly it is growing using the lines on your lolly stick.

9. When your baby oak tree has grown as tall as your hand it's best to put it outside in a bigger pot of compost – or you could even plant it in the ground.

Hints and tips:

● Not all acorns have enough energy in them to become trees, so put a few in the fridge to make sure you get one that grows.

● Acorns start growing in the spring after the cold of winter, and often need chilly weather before they will grow roots – that's why it's a good idea to put them in the fridge before planting them.

● Once your tree has grown big enough to move outside, you might still need to water it if the weather is very dry.

Keep adventuring:

If you enjoyed growing your own oak tree, why not try planting some other tree nuts too – conkers, hazelnuts and beech nuts all work well.

Owl Ice Cream

'Owl ice cream? Toowhit toowhoo!'
Are you ready to mix up your own owl ice cream?
Just remember this is for playing with, not for eating.

Adventure kit:

- 1.5kg plain flour
- 500ml baby oil
- A large bowl
- Small bowls
- Plastic tubs with lids
- An ice cream scoop
- Soil, leaves, grass, petals and sticks

What to do:

1. Mix the flour and baby oil together in a large bowl until all the oil has soaked into the flour. The mixture should hold its shape when you squeeze some in your hand, but otherwise be soft and crumbly.

2. Have fun squashing, squeezing and playing with your mixture, before dividing it between your plastic tubs.

3. Now make your pretend ice cream flavours, a different one for each tub. How about mixing in crumbly dry soil for chocolate chip, snipped-up green leaves for mint or colourful flower petals for tutti frutti? How many different ones can you think of?

4. Once you have all the flavours you want, it's time to get scooping! Fill your scoop with ice cream and to get a really good shape, press it into the scoop with your hand. Tap the scoop firmly onto your palm to get your ball of ice cream out.

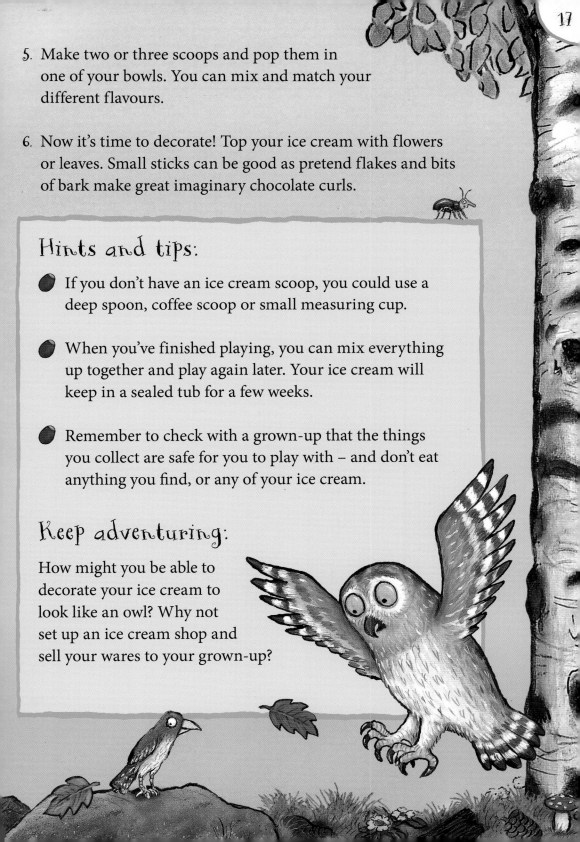

5. Make two or three scoops and pop them in one of your bowls. You can mix and match your different flavours.

6. Now it's time to decorate! Top your ice cream with flowers or leaves. Small sticks can be good as pretend flakes and bits of bark make great imaginary chocolate curls.

Hints and tips:

- If you don't have an ice cream scoop, you could use a deep spoon, coffee scoop or small measuring cup.

- When you've finished playing, you can mix everything up together and play again later. Your ice cream will keep in a sealed tub for a few weeks.

- Remember to check with a grown-up that the things you collect are safe for you to play with – and don't eat anything you find, or any of your ice cream.

Keep adventuring:

How might you be able to decorate your ice cream to look like an owl? Why not set up an ice cream shop and sell your wares to your grown-up?

Nutty Hide and Seek

The mouse found a nut and the nut was good.
How good are you at finding nuts – and hiding them?
Play this game with a friend to find out!

Adventure Kit: A conker, an acorn or another tree nut.

What to do:

1. Find a good place to play. It should be somewhere outside with lots of places you can hide a nut – on a tree stump, a patch of moss or next to a big rock.

2. Decide who will be the hider and who will be the seeker.

3. The hider should place the nut somewhere while the seeker closes their eyes, and doesn't peep. (It's best to leave your nut in the open rather than hiding it under anything, unless you want a really, really long game!)

4. Once the nut is ready, the hider can tell the seeker to start searching.

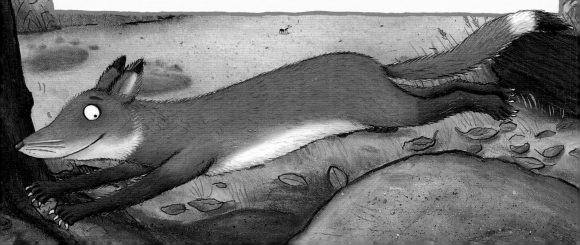

5. As the seeker moves around, the hider should give clues to help them. As the seeker gets closer and closer to the nut the hider should say 'warm . . . warmer . . . hot . . . boiling.' If the seeker moves away from the hiding place the hider should say 'cold . . . colder . . . freezing.'

6. Once the nut has been found, change over so that the hider is the seeker and the seeker is the hider.

Hints and tips:

● Start with some simple hiding places. Once you have the idea of the game you can start making the hiding places more difficult.

● You could try leaving some clues to help the seeker – perhaps an 'X' to mark the spot, a trail of green leaves, or some arrows made from sticks.

● Who can find the best hiding place for the nut? Perhaps you could time each other to see who is quickest at finding the nut?

Keep adventuring:

If you want to make the game trickier, try burying the nut or hiding it under something, but be sure to leave a clue or a symbol for your seeker. Why not try making a map to help the seeker find your hiding place? Pick a few landmarks to put on your map so the seeker can work out where to search.

Go on a Gruffalo Hunt

The Gruffalo likes the deep dark wood best of all, but you never know where you might spot him, so keep your eyes and ears open at all times.

Adventure Kit: Your eyes, ears and nose.

What to do:

Before you set out it is important to know what you are looking for. Can you remember what the Gruffalo looks like? His eyes are orange, his tongue is black and he has purple prickles all over his back . . .

When you're out and about, keep your wits about you and use your best detective skills to see what evidence you can uncover. Remember that animals like the Gruffalo are easily frightened – so step softly and try not to make too much noise.

Walk slowly and look around really carefully to give yourself the best chance of spotting things – get down on your hands and knees and see what you notice when you see the world from a different perspective.

Just like a lot of other animals that live in the deep dark wood, the Gruffalo is actually quite shy and hard to spot. However, animals always leave signs behind . . .

Can you find any of these signs that might mean that the Gruffalo has been nearby?

Scratches on trees. Could these have been made by his terrible claws?

Big piles of mud – or is it Gruffalo poo?

Slime on tree trunks and leaves. It might have been left by a snail or a slug . . . or perhaps the Gruffalo's poisonous wart!

Broken sticks on the ground and in the trees.

Fur caught in spiky bushes and brambles.

Footprints in soft ground. How big would a Gruffalo paw print be?

And don't forget to listen for movements in the undergrowth and use your nose to sniff for animal smells.

Keep adventuring:

Once you've got the hang of tracking a big animal like the Gruffalo, why not keep an eye out for other animal tracks and signs? You could try looking for signs of a little brown mouse – you can often see holes that mice might live in, little paths they have left in the grass or even nuts they have nibbled. Good luck!

Monkey Puzzle

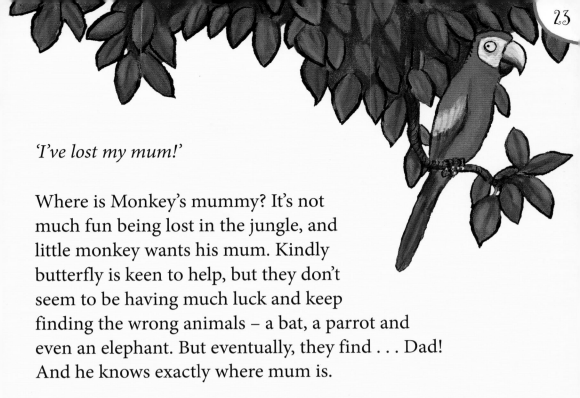

'I've lost my mum!'

Where is Monkey's mummy? It's not much fun being lost in the jungle, and little monkey wants his mum. Kindly butterfly is keen to help, but they don't seem to be having much luck and keep finding the wrong animals – a bat, a parrot and even an elephant. But eventually, they find . . . Dad! And he knows exactly where mum is.

Read on to fly like a bat, make your very own slithery snake, and head out on an exciting spider hunt.

Build a Butterfly Feeder

Butterflies, bees and other insects drink sweet nectar from flowers.
Make a butterfly feeder to see how many you can attract.

Adventure kit:

- An A4 sheet of paper
- Colouring pens or pencils
- Safety scissors
- A plastic bottle lid
- A teaspoon
- A cup
- A teaspoon of sugar
- A piece of kitchen paper
- Ten teaspoons of warm water

What to do:

1. First make your petals. Take your sheet of paper and fold it in half so the short sides meet. Then fold it in half again and then once more. Draw a big petal on one side, filling up as much of the space as you can without touching the edges.

2. Keeping the paper tightly folded, cut around your petal shape. Because you're cutting through all the layers at once, this will give you eight separate petals.

3. Now colour them in. Butterflies and other insects are attracted to flowers by their bright petals, so the more colourful the better.

4. Next use your scissors to cut three circles of kitchen paper to fit inside the bottle lid and put them in.

5. Take your bottle top and petals outside and find a flat place to build your feeder. Pop the bottle top in the centre and arrange the petals around it to make a beautiful flower.

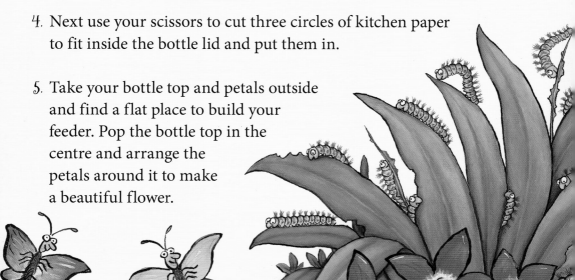

6. Now make the nectar. Put the warm water into the cup with the sugar and stir the mixture until all the sugar has dissolved.

7. Take the cup to your flower, and use the teaspoon to fill the bottle top with nectar. The kitchen paper will soak up the sugar water, making it easier for insects to feed. Your flower is now ready to feed a butterfly!

8. Find a spot a little way away from your feeder where you can sit and watch. It may take some time and you will need to be quiet and still, but keep watching and see who will be first to visit your flower . . .

Hints and tips:

- There are very few insects around in the winter. The best time of year to try this activity is from late spring through to early autumn.

- Try and put your feeder in the open so visiting butterflies and insects won't be in danger from birds hiding in nearby trees or bushes.

- If colouring isn't really your thing, you can try building a flower feeder with real petals that you find on the ground – just arrange them around your bottle top full of nectar.

Keep adventuring:

Can you make a record or draw a picture of the insects that visited your feeder? What happens if you change the colour or the size of your petals or the location of your flower?

Bat Wings

Find your own pair of wings and see if you can fly around just like a bat!

Adventure Kit: Two leafy fallen branches about the length of your arm, and a big space to run around in.

What to do:

1. First find yourself some fallen branches to be your bat wings. Leafy branches, bits of conifer, bracken or fern all work well. They should be quite light and flappy and have a good place for you to hold on to them.

2. Take one wing in each hand. Stretch up tall and raise your wings straight up in the air until you are standing on the very tips of your toes.

3. Bring your wings down with a big flap! Flap your arms up and down a few times to test out your wings.

4. Now start running with your new wings and see how fast you can go.

5. Once you've had a good fly you might feel ready for a rest. Find a spot where you can curl up to sleep, tucking your wings around you to keep yourself warm. When you've had a rest, stretch those wings out and you're all set to get flying again.

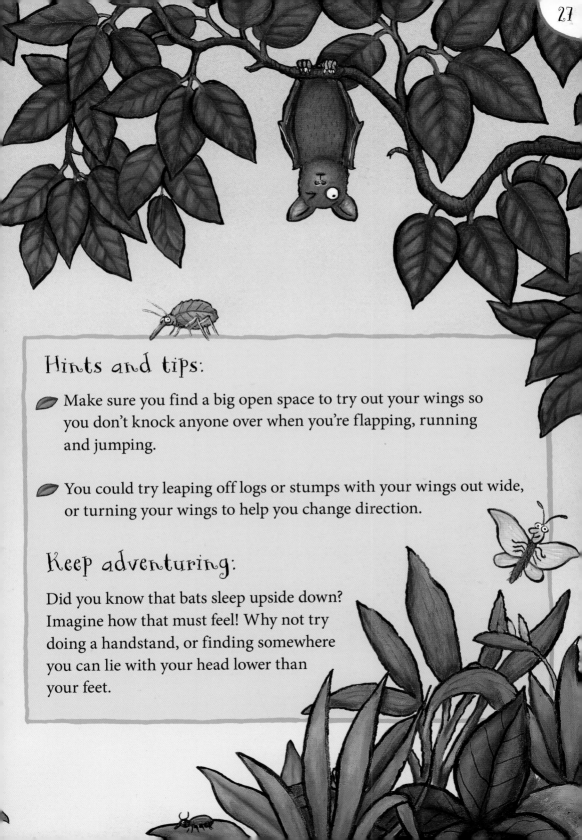

Hints and tips:

- Make sure you find a big open space to try out your wings so you don't knock anyone over when you're flapping, running and jumping.

- You could try leaping off logs or stumps with your wings out wide, or turning your wings to help you change direction.

Keep adventuring:

Did you know that bats sleep upside down? Imagine how that must feel! Why not try doing a handstand, or finding somewhere you can lie with your head lower than your feet.

Make an Elder Snake

'Mum doesn't look a bit like this. She doesn't slither about and hiss.'
Make yourself a slithery wooden snake.

Adventure kit:

- An elder tree or bush
- Secateurs
- A black pen
- Glue
- A skewer
- Red wool or ribbon
- Two pieces of string around 50cm long

What to do:

1. Find an elder tree or shrub that you are allowed to cut a few branches from. Elder bark is greyish brown and covered in warty little bumps. You can find it growing in hedgerows, woodlands and some wilder parks and gardens.

2. Look carefully to find young green branches and ask a grown-up to use the secateurs to cut two as long as your arm and at least as thick as their thumb.

3. Look at the cut end of your elder branch and you should be able to see a pale circle in the middle. This is called the pith. You should be able to squash it easily with a small stick.

4. Ask a grown-up to trim off any smaller branches and leaves, and cut the main branches into sections about 1.5cm long. You need 15-20 pieces.

5. Poke the skewer into the soft pith in the middle of each piece. Wiggle it about until the pith is pushed right out.

6. Use your skewer to poke around inside each piece until you have a clear hole through the centre. Some of your pieces might break, but you should still have plenty for a good snake.

7. Now build your snake! Thread a length of string through a piece of elder, using your skewer to push it through if you need to. Tie one end of the string around this piece to hold it in place.

8. Thread the rest of the string through each section in turn to build up your snake's body, then tie the final one in place as you did with the first section. This will be your snake's head.

9. Draw some eyes, then stick a small piece of red wool or ribbon underneath the eyes to make a tongue.

10. Tie the other length of string to your snake's head, then pull it along and watch as your snake slithers behind you.

Hints and tips:

- If you're struggling to get the pith out of a piece of elder, it may be that the branch is a little narrow. Try using a larger piece instead.

- You can wrap sticky tape around one end of your string to make it easier to poke through the holes.

Keep adventuring:

If you can't find any elder you could try making a snake with pieces of an old bamboo cane, or even with some pasta tubes. Not a fan of snakes? Perhaps it's a caterpillar instead!

Jumping Frogs

Monkey's mum isn't green and she doesn't croak, but she does leap about in the trees. Try this game to get your toys leaping about too!

Adventure Kit: A flat plank of wood around 50cm long, a small round log or a fat stick and some small soft toys.

What to do:

1. Find a big open space to play in.

2. Lay your plank over the log or stick so that it looks like a see-saw. The log should be in the middle and the plank should have one end touching the ground and one end in the air.

3. Place your soft toy (a frog if you have one) on the end of the plank that is touching the ground.

4. Stamp on the other end of the plank and watch your frog go leaping up into the sky.

Hints and tips:

🌿 Be sure to stand to the side of the plank when you fire your frog into the sky – that way the plank won't hit you in the knee and the frog won't hit you in the face!

🌿 Try moving the plank so the log is no longer in the middle. Does this make your frog jump higher or lower? Try playing with a bigger log or a fatter stick to see what happens.

Keep adventuring:

How high can you make your frog jump? Can you make him go over your head? Can you make him jump over a grown-up's head? Why not set up some lines on the ground to see how far you can make your frog jump?

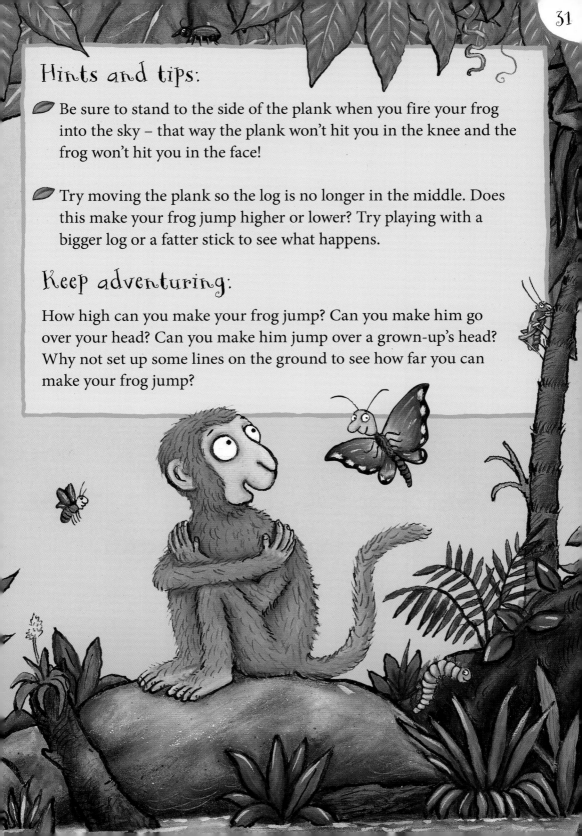

Parrot Kite

Make a colourful kite that really flies!

Adventure kit:

- Coloured A4 paper
- Pens
- Safety scissors
- A long ball of string
- Sticky tape
- A hole punch
- A small stick
- Long bits of grass,
  straw, wool or ribbon

What to do:

1. Take the A4 paper
   and fold it in half by bringing
   the two short sides together.

2. Lay the paper down with
   the fold facing you. Pick
   up the top left corner of
   the top piece, gently bend
   it over and stick it to the
   fold as shown.

3. Turn the paper over and lay it with the fold facing you. Pick up the top
   right corner and bring it down to the fold, sticking it in line with the
   corner from step 2. These are your parrot's wings.

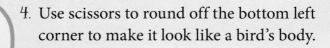

4. Use scissors to round off the bottom left
   corner to make it look like a bird's body.

5. Use your pens to give your parrot some eyes
   and a beak.

6. Use the hole punch to make a hole just above
   the fold between the beak and the wings. Feed
   your string through and tie it in place.

7. Tie the other end of the string to your stick and then
   wrap the rest of the string around it so you can let it
   out a little at a time when you're flying your kite.

8. Take the long bits of grass, straw, wool or ribbon and use some sticky tape to attach them to your kite to make a beautiful parrot tail.

9. Take your kite outside. Hold the string tightly in one hand, throw your kite into the air and let the wind catch it!

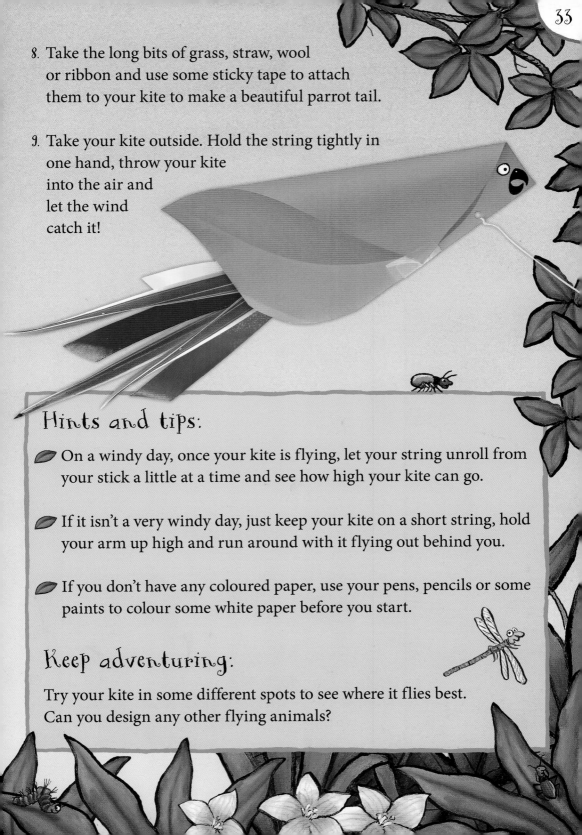

Hints and tips:

- On a windy day, once your kite is flying, let your string unroll from your stick a little at a time and see how high your kite can go.

- If it isn't a very windy day, just keep your kite on a short string, hold your arm up high and run around with it flying out behind you.

- If you don't have any coloured paper, use your pens, pencils or some paints to colour some white paper before you start.

Keep adventuring:

Try your kite in some different spots to see where it flies best. Can you design any other flying animals?

Spider and Cobweb Hunt

Try these tricks to help you spot a stunning spider web.

Adventure kit: Your eyes!

What to do:

Go to your favourite outdoor place. You will find spiders almost anywhere but a place with a few plants, stones or piles of wood is ideal. Spiders and their webs can be hard to see so take your time, look very carefully and go slowly so as not to miss anything . . .

Spiders spin webs to catch insects to eat, so look in a place where tasty insects are living.

A web needs to be attached to something. Try looking between the stalks of plants, in the branches of trees or on a stone wall.

It can be useful to get down low and look up towards the sky. Looking at something from a different viewpoint helps you spot new things.

A dewy morning is the perfect time for cobweb hunting. Water droplets in the air cling to the strands of the web making them easier to see.

Once you've found a cobweb...

- 🐝 What shapes and patterns can you see in it?
- 🐝 Can you see the spider that made the web?
- 🐝 Has the spider caught anything for lunch?

If you spot a spider...

- 🐝 What colour is it?
- 🐝 Can you count its legs?
- 🐝 Can you see its eyes?

Watch how the spider moves and see what happens if you lightly touch the web with a piece of grass.

Hints and tips:

🍃 Spider silk is incredibly strong but remember that you are a giant compared to the spider so do be careful. It's best not to touch the spiders or their webs at all, as your giant fingers and thumbs could easily hurt them even if you're being gentle.

Keep adventuring:

Spiders will spin a silk blanket around their eggs for protection. If you spot what looks like a lump of web it's likely to contain lots of baby spiders!

Room on the Broom

The witch had a cat and a very tall hat,
And long ginger hair which she wore in a plait.

The witch and her cat fly happily over forests, rivers and mountains on their broomstick until a stormy wind blows away her hat, bow and wand. A dog, a bird and a frog help the witch find her lost things but then they all want a ride on the broom too, until . . . SNAP! The broom breaks in two. And with a greedy dragon on the prowl, the witch's animal friends need a clever plan . . .

Turn the page to find out how to make your own wand and cast some spells, fly a mini broomstick and roar like a dragon!

Mini Broomsticks

There are lots of animals wanting a little room on the witch's broom. Why not make a mini broomstick so your toy animals can enjoy a ride too?

Adventure kit:

- Elastic bands
- Safety scissors
- Small toys
- A bunch of straw, hay or grass

What to do:

1. Go on a stick hunt – find one that you think is perfect for your broom handle. Will it be wobbly and knobbly or straight and smooth? It should be about the length of your arm, from fingertip to elbow.

2. Bunch up the straw or hay in your hand and wrap the elastic band around it to hold it together. This will make your broomstick tail.

3. Push the broom handle into the bunch of straw, wiggling it around until it feels firmly in place.

4. Use scissors to snip the straw or grass into the shape you want for your broomstick tail.

5. Hold up your broomstick and have a go at moving it through the air. Can you make it fly forwards and backwards, or loop-the-loop?

6. Pop one of your toys on the broom and hold it in place as you fly your broom around. How do they like zooming through the sky? Don't forget the sound effects. Whoosh!

7. Use elastic bands to attach more toys to your broomstick. Wrap the bands around the broom handle and tuck their feet or tails underneath. Is there room on the broom for all your favourites?

Hints and tips:

🍄 If you want your broom to look really magical, why not try painting it or decorating the handle with biodegradable glitter?

🍄 Remember to always take dead sticks from the ground rather than pulling living ones off the trees.

Keep adventuring:

Where will your toys fly off to? Do any of your animals need seats, nests or showers? If you can find some really big sticks, why not make a broom for yourself – you can make it exactly the same way, you'll just need a bit more of everything and you'll maybe need to tie the straw or hay to your broomstick with some string unless you can find a giant elastic band!

Marvellous Mud Spells

'Iggety, ziggety, zaggety, ZOOM!' The witch mixes up a magic spell in her cauldron. Try this recipe for some muddy, bubbly, fizzy fun.

Adventure kit:

- Some mud
- Water
- Bicarbonate of soda
- A pipette or a teaspoon
- Vinegar in a small bowl
- An egg cup, a yoghurt pot, or a small container

What to do:

1. Fill your egg cup or container with mud, adding a few drops of water to make the mud soft enough to stir around.

2. Make a shallow hole in the middle of your mud and pop in a spoonful of bicarbonate of soda.

3. Use a spoon to pull mud from the edges over the bicarbonate of soda.

4. Fill your pipette with vinegar. If you don't have a pipette, don't worry, just grab a teaspoon and fill that carefully instead.

5. Push the tip of the pipette into your egg cup and under the mud. Then squeeze the top of your pipette so that all the vinegar shoots into the egg cup. If you're using a spoon, tip all the vinegar into the middle of your egg cup.

6. Give everything a quick little stir with your spoon or a stick.

7. Stand back and watch your spell fizzing and bubbling away!

Hints and tips:

🍄 The magic happens when you mix the bicarbonate of soda and the vinegar together – so make sure you keep these ingredients apart when you're not casting a spell.

🍄 Add a few drops of paint or food colouring to your egg cup if you want your spell to bubble in a different colour.

Keep adventuring:

Try and think of some magic words to say over your bubbling spells. What will each of your spells do? Are your spells nasty or nice? How about adding a few flower petals for a love charm or some puddle water for a pongy potion? Amaze your friends with your magical powers!

Magic Wands

All serious spell casters need a magic wand. Just be sure you hold tight to yours when you're whizzing about on your broomstick!

Adventure kit:

- Ribbon or string
- Safety scissors
- A plastic bowl or tub
- PVA glue
- A paintbrush
- Natural things to decorate your wand: petals, leaves and moss

What to do:

1. Go on a stick hunt – find the most interesting, knobbly and gnarly one you can. The weirder and more wonderful the stick, the better.

2. Check your stick is the right size for a wand by practising some swishing and spell casting – you can break bits off to make it smaller if you need to. Decide which end should be the handle and which end the magic will come out of.

3. Tie a piece of ribbon or string around the handle of your wand. You could cover the whole handle by wrapping it in string or ribbon or just tie a bow for decoration.

4. Use scissors to cut the things you have collected for decorating your wand into tiny pieces. Collect the pieces in your plastic bowl. Mix in some biodegradable glitter too if you have it.

5. Use your paintbrush to brush glue on to the top part of the wand, above the handle.

6. Sprinkle the chopped up leaves and petals over the gluey bits. Keep turning the wand to make sure it will be beautiful all over.

7. Give your wand a little time to dry and then you are ready for some serious spell casting. Who will you turn into a frog today?

Hints and tips:

🍄 Dry sticks work best for gluing and painting.

🍄 Always take dead sticks from the ground rather than pulling living ones off the trees.

🍄 Take care to give yourself plenty of space when you're casting spells so you don't accidentally poke any other witches or wizards in the eye.

Keep adventuring:

Now you have a beautiful magic wand, you can practise casting super spells. Start by making simple shapes in the air such as circles, triangles and spirals. Then put a couple of shapes together. A circle followed by a zig zag, or a triangle and then a square. Why not try saying the spell to conjure up a new broomstick? And remember, the way you wave your wand is very important – one extra swish and you could end up as a slug!

Muddy Monsters

Dragons are scary but a muddy monster is the most fearsome creature of all. Make your own and see who you can scare.

Adventure kit:

- Some mud
- Water
- A stirring stick or spoon
- Sticks, leaves and stones
- An old towel
- An old mixing bowl or container that can get muddy

What to do:

1. Put some mud and water into your mixing bowl and start stirring. You want your mud to be thick enough to squash into a ball so add the water a little at a time until it's just right. If your mixture gets too sloppy, just add in a bit more mud.

2. Get your sticks, leaves and stones ready. You might want to break some of them up into small sizes to be just right for arms, legs, spines, tails or teeth.

3. Get stuck in! Grab a handful of mud and squeeze it into the shape you want to make the body of your monster.

4. Pop your monster body somewhere flat and then add a head – or two! Once you are happy with the shape of your monster give your muddy hands a wipe on the old towel. Then use your sticks and leaves to give your monster body all its features. Arms, legs, tails, teeth, claws or pincers – you decide . . .

Hints and tips:

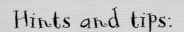 Pebbles or green leaves make great monster eyes.

Try building your monster on a big leaf so you can move it around if you need to.

Keep adventuring:

Where's the best place to put your muddy monster so that it scares off any passing dragons? How many different kinds can you make? Can you build a monster family? Why not try your monsters out on your grown-up to see if they're scary enough?

Build a Magical Fire

Get cracking and see if you can make your very own magical fire.

Adventure Kit: A place with lots of sticks on the ground.

What to do:

1. Gather a pile of sticks to break up. You'll need at least ten sticks of different sizes, from the thickness of your little finger to the thickness of your arm and they should be at least as long as you are tall.

2. Make sure you're carrying your sticks safely: hold one end in your hand and have the other end dragging on the ground behind you.

3. Once you've finished collecting, it's time to break your sticks into smaller pieces. There are two good ways of doing this:

☆ Use your knee for small, thin sticks. Hold the stick in both hands, with your hands shoulder-width apart. Lift up your knee so it's between the stick and your body, then push with your knee as you draw your hands back.

☆ Use your foot for medium and big sticks. Lay a thick stick or log on the ground. Place one end of your stick on it at a right angle to look like the letter T with the other end on the ground. Put one foot on the end touching the ground and use your other foot to stamp on the middle part of the stick.

4. Keep going until you've broken up all your sticks into short lengths. They should be about as long as your arm from elbow to wrist.

5. Clear a circle on the ground by sweeping any leaves to one side. Starting with your thickest sticks, build a pyramid shape by leaning them up against each other. Then fill in the gaps with smaller sticks until you're happy with how your fire looks.

6. Now try putting a handful of dry grass or leaves on top to make it look like it's really alight!

Hints and tips:

🍄 Collect your sticks from the ground. Living branches still on trees are full of wet sap so are often bendy and difficult to snap. Sticks on the ground are more likely to be dry inside, making them easier to break.

🍄 If a stick doesn't snap, it may be that it's fallen from a tree quite recently and is still too bendy – or it might be too thick and strong. If a stick doesn't snap after a few tries, just swap it for another one.

Keep adventuring:

Why not mix leaves and water in a cauldron or bucket and pretend it's bubbling on your fire, or put leaves on a stick and pretend to toast them?

Roar Like a Dragon

The witch's half-broomstick flew into a cloud,
And the witch heard a roar that was scary and loud.
Find the dragon inside you and practise your roar . . .

Adventure kit: Your voice!

What to do:

Find a good place to stand. What about somewhere high so your roar can be heard far and wide?

Adopt your roaring pose. Stand with your legs apart, your shoulders back and your chin raised.

Now you need to warm up your voice. Here are a few things you can try . . .

click your tongue

hum

make some quiet noises

make some loud noises

gently stretch your lips, cheeks and neck

try saying a tongue twister

Now . . . can you make a little growl in the back of your throat?

Get ready to roar!

☆ Start as quietly as you can with the smallest roar possible.
☆ Now a little bit louder.
☆ Louder still . . .
☆ . . . and now as loud as you can!

How many different roar sounds can you make?

How might a dragon say 'Hi' and how might a dragon tell you he's cross?!

Which is scarier, a roar or a growl?

Why not have a roaring competition with your friends to see who can roar the loudest?

How does a baby dragon sound, and how about a daddy dragon?

Hints and tips:

🍄 Remember that dragons aren't allowed in houses – so save your roaring practice for outside.

🍄 If you're not sure how to roar, think of the sound a lion, a tiger or a bear might make.

Charlie Cook's Favourite Book

Once upon a time there was a boy called Charlie Cook
Who curled up in a cosy chair and read his favourite book . . .

Charlie Cook is reading about a pirate, who is reading about
Goldilocks, who is reading about a knight . . . and so on!
Everyone has a favourite book, including astronauts, ghosts,
crocodiles and even a team of royal cake bakers.

Who will you be today? Be a pirate and make your very own
boat, build a nest just like a bird or roll up your sleeves and
be a muddy chef!

Make a Massive Mud Cake

The Queen's birthday cake is the biggest the world has ever seen!
How big will your mud cake be?

Adventure kit:

- Water
- A spade
- A plate
- An old towel
- Three plastic containers: big, medium and small
- Sticks, stones, petals, leaves and grass

What to do:

1. Find a place with lots of mud that you are allowed to dig in and make messy.

2. Use your spade to turn the mud over and break it up into lots of little bits.

3. Dig out a few handfuls of dry mud and keep them aside for later. Then add water to your mud patch a splash at a time until it's soft enough to squash in your hands.

4. Sprinkle a handful of dry mud into each of your plastic containers. This will help the mud cakes slide out of them later.

5. Fill your containers with soft wet mud, being sure to push it into all the corners. Make the tops nice and flat with a spade or your hands.

6. To make the bottom layer of your cake, hold the biggest container in two hands and quickly turn it upside down onto the plate (imagine you're making a sandcastle). Give the container a few sharp taps with your spade and gently lift it. The mud cake should slide out. If your container is very heavy or your hands are slippery, ask a grown-up to help.

7. Once you are happy with the bottom layer, turn out the next biggest container on top of the first to make your middle layer.

8. Now see if you can manage a final top layer. This should be the smallest of all the containers. It might be easier to turn out your layers onto a hard surface and then lift them into position on the cake with your spade or your hands so that all the layers don't get squashed.

9. Once the layers are in place, you're ready to start decorating. Give your hands a wipe on the old towel and then use sticks, stones, petals and leaves to make your cake look fit for a queen!

Hints and tips:

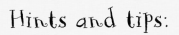 You'll probably find lots of worms while you're busy digging in the mud. Be very gentle with them and pop them to one side of your hole so you don't hurt them.

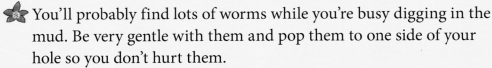 If you don't have any containers, then just build with your hands.

Old cake tins or cookie cutters can make great mud shapes.

Keep adventuring:

Why not see what other magnificent mud things you can make? You could try making tiny cupcakes to go around the edge of your masterpiece or use big leaves to make mud sandwiches. What about a muddy sauce? Just remember not to eat any of the things you make, no matter how good they look!

Build a Cork Boat

All good pirates need a ship to sail.
Build yourself a little boat and head off on an adventure!

Adventure kit:

- Two corks
- Two elastic bands
- A medium-sized leaf
- A scrap of thick cardboard
- A small skinny stick
  (about the length of
  your biggest finger)
- A washing-up bowl or a
  large sandwich box full
  of water, or a puddle

What to do:

1. Place the two corks beside each other and wrap an elastic band around both of them to hold them together at one end (two sets of hands are good for this bit so ask a grown-up to help you).

2. Wrap your second elastic band around the other end of the corks to make your boat.

3. Wiggle your stick in between the two corks so that it is sticking straight up. If your corks are held together really tightly you may need a grown-up to pull the corks apart for you while you pop the stick in. This is your mast.

4. Push the mast through the top and bottom of a leaf to make a sail. Now put your boat into the water to see if it floats . . .

5. If your boat tips over when you put it in the water it's probably because your mast is too long and heavy. Try snapping the top off your stick to make it shorter and lighter.

6. Blow on your boat to see if you can get it to travel to the other side of the water.

7. Wave the scrap of cardboard backwards and forwards really fast to make a sea storm. Your boat should go dashing across the water with all that wind behind it! Will your boat come through the storm or will it capsize?

Hints and tips:

❀ These boats are also really fun to play with in the bath.

❀ Did you know . . . corks float because they are less dense than water. Wood and ice are also less dense than water and so are good for floating too. Stones are usually more dense than water and so they sink.

Keep adventuring:

Can you make a bigger boat using more corks and more rubber bands? What shape floats best and can you make a boat big enough to carry a little toy? Why not see what you can find in your park or garden that floats and sinks?

Planet Craters

Craters are shallow holes on the surface of a planet or moon
that are made when it is hit by a rock travelling through space.
Get ready to make a crater!

Adventure kit:

- Flour
- A sieve or a spoon
- An old tray
- Three tablespoons
  of cocoa powder
- Four stones of
  different sizes

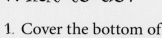

What to do:

1. Cover the bottom of your tray with
   around 1cm of flour. Gently pat it
   down with your hands to make it nice
   and flat.

2. Use the sieve or a spoon to cover the
   flour with a thin layer of cocoa powder.
   This will be the surface of your planet.

3. Take one of your stones, stand above the tray, open your hand and let
   the stone drop onto the surface of your planet.

4. Check out the crater you made! The stone should have broken
   through the top layer of your planet (the cocoa powder) and made a
   hole in the rock underneath (the flour). Did the stone bounce out or
   is it still in the hole? Can you see the patterns made by the impact?

5. Try making another crater with a
   different sized stone.

6. Once you've dropped all your stones a few times and the surface of your planet is all churned up, flatten it down with your hands and spread another thin layer of cocoa powder on top so that you can play again.

7. Why not try dropping your stones from different heights by crouching down, stretching up tall or even standing on a log? What height makes the most impressive crater and do big rocks or small stones work best?

Hints and tips:

❀ Any kind of powder will work for this activity, you just need two different colours to make it fun – and be sure to ask permission before you take anything from the cupboard.

❀ Be sure to only ever drop your stones, don't throw them.

Keep adventuring:

Can you make craters on your planet surface with other natural items? Do pinecones, sticks or conkers work too? Can you recreate a meteor shower by using a handful of pebbles? You can try making craters in lots of different places like a sandpit, a patch of earth, a beach, or around a muddy puddle. What do your craters look like in different places?

Dig for Treasure

At last he found a treasure chest, and in it was a book . . .
Digging for treasure is always fun. What will you find?

Adventure kit:

- A bucket or basket
- A trowel
- Treasure: coins, conkers, pebbles or pinecones

What to do:

1. First decide where your treasure is going to be buried. A sand pit works well if you have one or you can fill a large container with grass cuttings or woodchip, or even just heap them up into a big pile.

2. Ask a grown-up or a friend to hide the treasure for you. Cover your eyes and be sure to ask them to bury it all nice and deep so it isn't too easy to find!

3. Now grab your bucket and trowel and get ready to start digging. As soon as you uncover some treasure, pop it in your bucket – how long will it take you to fill your bucket all the way to the top?

4. Once you've found it all, simply bury it and play again. How fast can you find it this time?

Hints and tips:

✿ If you are hunting in grass or woodchip, small treasure can be tricky to spot. Larger coins or pebbles work well.

✿ Stones painted gold and silver make excellent treasure.

Keep adventuring:

It might be that your treasure is grubby after being buried, so why not get out the soap and water to make it all shiny and clean again. You might also need to sort the treasure once it's been dug up. Can you make piles of different colours, shapes or sizes? You could also play treasure hide and seek with your friends. Try making a treasure map with an X to mark the spot where the treasure is hidden.

The Best Nest

The birds in this story have a competition to see whose nest is best. All birds build their nests slightly differently . . . but how will you build yours?

Adventure kit: Grass, bendy ivy stems or thin flexible sticks as long as your arm, and bits to line your nest – moss, petals or even old socks!

What to do:

1. Start by making a frame for your nest. Take a piece of grass, a stem or stick and hold it about one third of the way down in your left hand. Take hold of the bottom end of the stem or stick in your right hand. Bend it up and place it in your left hand to create a circle.

2. You should now be holding a circle with a third of the stem sticking up from your left hand. Take this top third in your right hand and weave it in and out of the circle until you get to the end.

3. Still holding tightly with your left hand, take a new stem and weave it in and out of the circle until you get to the end.

4. Once you've done this a few times you should be able to let go of the stems in your left hand and the weaving should hold the circle together.

5. Using both hands, keep on weaving more grass, sticks and leaves into the frame of your nest until you're happy with it.

6. Once the frame of your nest is good and strong, you'll need to think about what to put in the middle to make it soft and comfy. How about lining your nest with moss or leaves?

7. Once your nest is finished, test it out. Little stones make good eggs, or some of your toys might even be small enough to sit inside.

Hints and tips:

🌸 If you're not happy with the way your nest looks, just take out all the sticks and other bits, fiddle with your nest frame and start again.

🌸 Once your nest is finished, why not see if you can find a low tree or a bush to pop it in – you never know who might be looking for a new home!

Keep adventuring:

How many different nests can you come up with? Play with a friend and have a competition, to see which nest is best. Perhaps you could even make some medals to present to the best ones.

Crocodile Puddle Hunting

Crocodiles sometimes come on land when they get fed up with fish . . .
Will you be lucky enough to catch one?

Adventure Kit: A stick, some wet weather and lots of puddles!

What to do:

First make your crocodile fishing rod. Hunt around for the best stick
for the job. Do you want one that's short and thick or long with leaves on
the end? All fishing rods are slightly different so take your time and find
the perfect one for you.

Now find some crocodiles!
Here are some things you can try . . .

Watch carefully for
splashes and spray. Could
this be a crocodile?

Use your rod to
gently prod each puddle.
Will there be anything moving
beneath the water?

Try plopping a few
stones into the puddle or
floating something on the surface
to see if any crocodiles can be
tempted to the top.

For really
stubborn crocodiles you
might need some bait. Find a
tasty-looking leaf, poke it on the
end of your rod and then
prod your puddle.

Give your rod a
good jiggle in the water
to wake any sleeping
crocodiles.

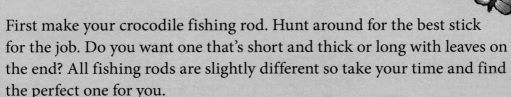

Remember that crocodiles love deep muddy puddles. Why not use a stick to check how deep a puddle is before you start fishing in it?

- Find a long stick and hold it upright in your hand.
- Put it straight down into the puddle until you feel the bottom.
- Carefully pull the stick out and look at the mark the water has left on it. This tells you how deep the puddle is and whether there is likely to be a crocodile lurking beneath the surface.

Do be careful . . . crocodiles can be grumpy when they first wake up so make sure you're always ready to drop your stick and run to safety! Can you jump over your puddle in case you need to make a quick getaway?

Hints and tips:

- If there are lots of crocodile hunters fishing at once, take care not to poke each other with your rods.

- Don't run with a stick in your hand in case you fall over and hurt yourself.

Keep adventuring:

What other watery animals might you find in a puddle? Sharks, turtles, or the Loch Ness monster? What might you need to tempt them out?

First published 2021 by Macmillan Children's Books
an imprint of Pan Macmillan
The Smithson, 6 Briset Street, London EC1M 5NR
Associated companies throughout the world
www.panmacmillan.com
ISBN: 978-1-5290-2050-2
Text copyright © Julia Donaldson 2021
Illustrations copyright © Axel Scheffler 2021
Activities created by Little Wild Things
Based on the bestselling picture books *The Gruffalo*, *Monkey Puzzle*, *Room on the Broom* and
Charlie Cook's Favourite Book by Julia Donaldson and Axel Scheffler
Moral rights asserted.

1 3 5 7 9 8 6 4 2

A CIP catalogue record for this book is available from the British Library.

Printed in China